KS1
Success

PRACTICE TEST PAPERS

Writing &
Spelling

Laura Griffiths

Contents

KEY STAGE 1
Levels 1–3

Introduction

Writing &
Spelling

Introduction

Introduction

Instructions on using
the Practice Test Papers

Understanding Assessment

What is assessment?
Teacher assessment will form the main part of your child's result at the end of Key Stage 1 (at the age of 7). However, tests and tasks help to validate the teacher's own assessment.

What are the children tested on?
All children study the National Curriculum from Year 1. At the end of Year 2, the tests will assess your child's knowledge, skills and understanding in the programmes of study that they have followed from Year 1.

In English the programme of study covers three areas:
English 1: Speaking and Listening
English 2: Reading
English 3: Writing

What tests will my child take?
Teacher assessment for seven-year-olds covers:

- reading
- writing
- speaking and listening
- maths
- science

These assessments take account of how your child performed in Key Stage 1 tasks and tests. The tasks and tests cover:

- reading
- writing (including handwriting and spelling)
- maths

The tasks and tests are informal and can be taken at a time the school chooses, although they usually take place towards the end of Year 2. The tasks and tests last for less than three hours altogether and the results help to inform the teacher's overall assessment of your child. No statutory testing is carried out at Key Stage 1.

Can my child fail a test?
It is important that children understand they are not going to 'pass' or 'fail' the test – it will just show what they have learned and what they can do.

Preparing your Child for Tests

These practice test papers prepare your child for school tests by giving them the confidence of knowing the sort of questions they will experience.

These practice test papers will also help you to assess how your child is doing at school. They will give you an indication of your child's strengths and weaknesses, and how you can help them.

How can you improve your child's score?
- Mark the papers.
- Look at what your child got wrong and talk it through with them.
- Let your child do the test again.
- Remember, keep practising the things they are weaker at. For example, if it is joining their handwriting or using punctuation, work further on these.
- Try to encourage your child not to throw away marks, by reading a question carefully and checking their answer.

About these Practice Test Papers

In this book, there are three separate sets of writing and spelling tests.

The writing tests comprise two writing tasks, one longer and one shorter. The tasks cover different styles of writing.

For your child to achieve their best result, it is advisable to give them only one task in a day.

The long task should take approximately 45 minutes, not including planning, and the short task should take approximately 30 minutes, not including planning.

The Long Writing Task

The specific writing tasks vary each year. The long task is usually selected from the following text types.

1 **A personal recount:** This writing would be the child recounting something they have done at school – for example, "The day we visited the police horses".

2 **Informative writing:** This is factual writing – for example, information about a dinosaur.

3 **Instructions:** This would be an explanation of how to do or make something – for example, a moving puppet.

4 **Extending and adapting stories:** This would include continuing a story – for example, writing the story ending or writing a story using the same characters from a familiar story but within a different setting.

5 **Letter writing:** This could be a letter to a character in a story (for example, Goldilocks), or to a famous person (for example, Florence Nightingale).

6 **Expressing opinions:** This could be writing about whether the toys that Grandma played with when she was a child are more exciting than those of today.

How to Administer the Long Task to your Child

Test A: Long Task – Letter writing

Read Gran and Grandpa's letter to your child. Discuss the content of the letter.

To help children think through their own ideas, it might be useful to ask them the following questions to support their writing:
a) Where do you think Gran and Grandpa live?
b) Do you think Gran and Grandpa miss James?
c) Why are Gran and Grandpa asking about his school?

Direct your child to the planning sheets and encourage them to write down their ideas.

Your child should not spend long on the planning sheets. It is just to support their writing and will not be marked.

When your child has completed their planning sheets and understood what the task is, they should begin writing the letter on a separate sheet of paper.

Most children can complete this piece of writing in 45 minutes and this timing should not normally be exceeded.

Your child should write independently, trying their best with spelling, handwriting and punctuation.

Encourage your child to use interesting vocabulary which is appropriate to the task, reader and purpose.

Test B: Long Task – Continuing a story

Read the story to your child and check they understand it. To help children think through their own ideas, it might be useful to ask them the following questions to support their writing:
a) Where is Katie going?
b) What might happen at the party?
c) How will your story end?

When your child understands the task, follow the same process as Test A. Direct them to the planning sheets to complete and then ask them to write their story on a separate sheet of paper.

Test C: Long Task – Story writing

Read the story of the hare and the tortoise to your child. Discuss the moral at the end of the story and ask them to give you ideas as to what it means.

Explain the task to them and discuss other animals that could be used.

When your child has an idea and feels confident with the writing, follow the same process as Tests A and B.

Assessing your Child's Score for the Long Task

You will need to assess three aspects of your child's writing:

1 Sentence structure.
2 Punctuation.
3 Composition and effect.

Each of these three aspects of your child's writing is divided into a number of bands which represent the level of achievement that your child has attained. For guidance, please refer to pages 49 and 50 of the Answers and Mark Scheme.

Please use the marking sheet on page 11 to record the marks. Where there is a choice of two or three different marks, use your judgement to decide if your child has fully achieved the objective or just partially.

When marking your child's writing, you must decide into which band it fits best. To help you decide which band your child's work falls into, please refer to the annotated children's writing on pages 51 to 54 of the Answers and Mark Scheme.

The Short Writing Task

In school assessments, the specific writing task varies each year. The short task could be selected from the following text types.

1   **Report writing:** This is writing about something the child has read. They would be expected to use appropriate vocabulary and to sequence ideas correctly.

2   **Writing instructions:** This could be, for example, how to play a game, how to bake a cake or writing rules.

3   **Note-taking:** This is writing where the child is expected to make simple notes from non-fiction texts, using headings, sub-headings and captions.

How to Administer the Short Task to your Child

Test A: Short Task – Postcard

Remind your child of the letter they wrote to Gran and Grandpa. Explain the task of writing a postcard. To support your child with their content, it is a good idea to give them an opportunity to share their thoughts orally.

Remind your child before they begin that they must write independently, making a sensible guess at any unknown spellings. Encourage them to use punctuation to make the meaning of their writing clear.

When they are ready to begin, direct them to the template of the postcard on page 21. They may like to put an address on the card, although this will not be marked.

Test B: Short Task – Recipe for making a cake

Before you start this activity, it will help your child if you show them a recipe for making a cake, or better still actually make one with them! This will give your child a good idea of the ingredients and method.

Direct your child to the planning sheet. Read the headings together and ask them to write down their ideas. Remind them not to spend too long on the planning.

When your child has completed the planning sheet, they should begin writing the recipe.

Test C: Short Task – Writing rules

Administer this test in the same way as Test A. Remind your child of the story of the hare and the tortoise. Discuss races and what rules are needed. Ask your child to write down rules for a successful school sports day.

All of the short tasks should take approximately 30 minutes to complete.

Assessing your Child's Score for the Short Task

You will need to assess two aspects of your child's writing:

1   Sentence structure and punctuation.
2   Composition and effect.

These two aspects of your child's writing are divided into a number of bands which represent the level of achievement that your child has attained. For guidance, please refer to pages 55 and 56 of the Answers and Mark Scheme.

Please use the marking sheet on page 12 to record the marks. Where there is a choice of two different marks, use your judgement to decide if your child has fully achieved the objective or just partially.

When marking your child's writing, you must decide into which band it fits best. To help you decide which band your child's work falls into, please refer to the annotated children's writing on pages 57 to 59 of the Answers and Mark Scheme.

The Spelling Test

Your child will be tested on 20 words. Some of these words will be easier than others.

What to do

Give the spelling test to your child. Explain that they will hear the story read aloud and when they come to a missing word they need to write the correct spelling.

Encourage your child to follow the passage on their test sheet, while you read the complete passage at a speed appropriate to your child.

Then read the passage again, more slowly this time, pausing at the gaps to allow your child to fill in the missing words. The first word is a practice and no marks are awarded for this word.

The words in bold type are the spellings that your child needs to write down.
Begin the test. You may repeat the target spellings once.

When your child has completed the spelling test, add up the total score (out of 20, excluding the practice question). Your child must spell the entire word correctly to gain a mark.

Marking the Tests and Assessing Levels

You can fill in your child's results in the tables below. Please refer to guidance and writing examples in the pull-out Answers and Mark Scheme for how to assess your child's performance.

Long Task Marking Sheet

Band A Sentence structure	Band B Punctuation	Band C Composition and effect

Total marks for the Long Task:

Set A: _____   Set B: _____   Set C: _____

Short Task Marking Sheet

Band D Sentence structure and punctuation	Band E Composition and effect

Total marks for the Short Task:

Set A: _____   Set B: _____   Set C: _____

Handwriting

There is no separate test to assess your child's handwriting. This makes it much easier! A score out of 3 will be given, by assessing the handwriting from the writing tasks. Please refer to page 60 of the Answers and Mark Scheme.

Spelling Test Marking Sheet

Your child will have a score out of 20. Use the table below to convert this score into a mark out of 7.

Number of correct words	0–3	4–7	8–11	12–14	15–16	17–18	19–20
Marks	1	2	3	4	5	6	7

The Overall Writing Level

You will now have separate scores for your child's writing. Insert these scores into the grid below.

	Set A	Set B	Set C
Long Task (out of 18)			
Short Task (out of 12)			
Handwriting (out of 3)			
Spelling (out of 7)			
Total score (out of 40)			

Please use the table below to convert your child's score into a National Curriculum level.

Score out of 40	National Curriculum level
0–8	Level 1 not achieved
9–17	Level 1 achieved
18–22	Level 2c achieved
23–27	Level 2b achieved
28–32	Level 2a achieved
33–40	Level 3 achieved

Please note: these tests are only a guide to the level your child can achieve and cannot guarantee the same level is achieved at Key Stage 1.

How well has my child done in these tests?

The results show whether or not your child has reached the expected National Curriculum level at the age of 7.

Level	Aged 7
Level 1	Below average
Level 2 Level 2c Level 2b Level 2a	At level expected
Level 3	Excellent
Level 4	Exceptional
Level 5	
Level 6	
Level 7	
Level 8	

What do the levels mean?

When your child's writing paper is marked, the correct marks are collated to give your child an overall score. This score is then matched to a National Curriculum level.

The government target for pupils at the end of Year 2 is to achieve Level 2. Some pupils will be working below this level and achieve Level 1, whilst other pupils will be working above the expected level and achieve Level 3.

Set
A

KEY STAGE 1
Levels 1–3

Planning Sheets
& Writing Tasks

Writing

Dear James

Planning Sheets & Writing Tasks

Dear James

Instructions:

- see page 6 (Long Writing Task) and page 8 (Short Writing Task) for details on how to administer the writing tasks

- find a quiet place where your child can sit down and complete the writing tasks undisturbed

- make sure your child has all the necessary equipment to complete the writing tasks

- make sure your child knows how to plan each task using the planning sheets

- when your child has completed the planning sheet, go through it together

- your child then begins the writing task on a separate sheet of lined paper

- check how your child has done using pages 49–62 of the Answers and Mark Scheme

Time:

Take as long as necessary but aim to complete the Long Writing Task in 45 minutes and the Short Writing Task in 30 minutes.

	Max. Mark	Actual Mark
Score	33	....

First name ....

Last name ....

Dear James

Instructions: This stimulus material is very similar to what your child will be given in school tests. The idea of it is to set the scene of the task and help your child to become inspired with their writing. You should read the stimulus material to your child. Ensure they understand it.

Dear James,

How are you? It has been ages since we last saw you.

Grandpa has just finished digging his new vegetable patch and hopefully we will be planting some potatoes soon. It is wonderful spending time outside now that the weather is so warm.

How is school going, James? We really do miss hearing your news now that you live so far away. It would be lovely if you could come and stay with us for a week in September.

Looking forward to hearing from you soon.

Love Gran and Grandpa
x x x

Long Writing Task

Now you have read *Dear James*, you are going to write a letter replying to Gran and Grandpa. Before you write the letter, plan your reply by thinking about:

1   how to start your letter

2   how to end your letter

Write down how James might be feeling.

_____

_____

_____

_____

Write down what James might be doing at school.

_____

_____

_____

_____

Write down an answer to the invitation to stay in September.

_____

_____

_____

_____

Write down three questions James could ask Gran and Grandpa.

_____

_____

_____

_____

_____

_____

_____

Read through your plan and think about what you have written. Now write your letter.

Short Writing Task

You are going to imagine James has gone to stay with his Gran and Grandpa and he is sending a postcard back home. You are going to write the postcard.

Before you write the postcard, plan what you will write by thinking about:

One exciting thing James has done.

_____

_____

_____

What the weather is like.

_____

_____

_____

How James feels.

_____

_____

_____

Read through your plan and think about what you have written. Now write the postcard.

Writing Template for the Postcard

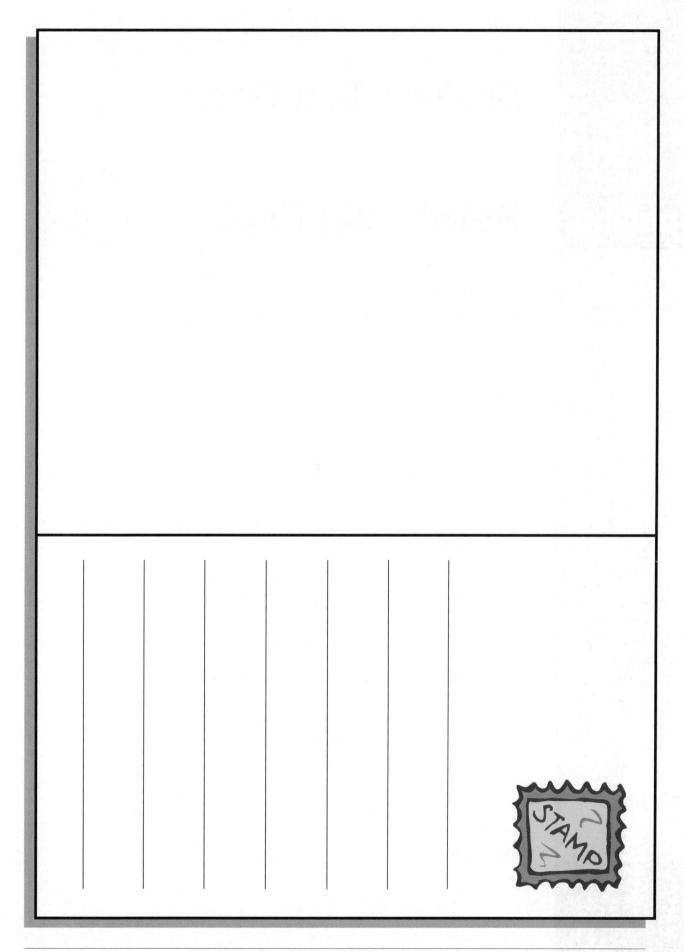

Set

A

KEY STAGE 1
Levels 1–3

Spelling Test
Paper

Spelling

Pete's Big Feet

Spelling Test Paper

Pete's Big Feet

Instructions:

- see page 10 for details on how to administer the test

- find a quiet place where you can sit down with your child

- make sure you have all the necessary equipment to complete the test paper

- read the short piece of text on page 63 to your child twice in its entirety

- during the first reading, your child should not write anything on the test paper

- during the second reading, pause after each word to be tested (shown in bold type), to enable your child to write the word in the gap on the test paper

- see page 64 for the spelling test mark conversion chart

Time:

Take as long as necessary to complete the test paper.

	Max.	**Number of words correct**
Score	20	....

First name ....

Last name ....

Say "Hi!" to Pete. He is _____**ever**_____ so sweet. *(practice question)*

He is _____ mean and _____ smiles at _____ he meets.

He remembers to say _____ and thank you, too. At _____, Pete likes to help _____ _____ his street. He tidies up garden weeds and sweeps floors for them.

When it is sunny, Pete _____ to fish at Wheat Field Stream.

But his favourite meal is not fish. It is lean meat _____ peas. And if he has a treat, it has to be cheese.

You see, Pete likes the same _____ as _____ _____.

He loves _____ with mates and _____ movies. He tries to be neat and tidy in his best _____ jeans.

Above his knees, Pete _____ like _____ you _____ meet. But _____ the knees, he makes some squeal.

"Are those real feet?" some say.

Others ask "Can I have a feel? Wow, _____ feet are unreal!"

You see, Pete has big, no, huge, no, giant-sized feet!

Planning Sheets & Writing Tasks

Katie

Instructions:

- see pages 6–7 (Long Writing Task) and page 8 (Short Writing Task) for details on how to administer the writing tasks

- find a quiet place where your child can sit down and complete the writing tasks undisturbed

- make sure your child has all the necessary equipment to complete the writing tasks

- make sure your child knows how to plan each task using the planning sheets

- when your child has completed the planning sheet, go through it together

- your child then begins the writing task on a separate sheet of lined paper

- check how your child has done using pages 49–62 of the Answers and Mark Scheme

Time:

Take as long as necessary but aim to complete the Long Writing Task in 45 minutes and the Short Writing Task in 30 minutes.

	Max. Mark	**Actual Mark**
Score	33	....

First name ....

Last name ....

Instructions: This stimulus material is very similar to what your child will be given in school tests. The idea of it is to set the scene of the task and help your child to become inspired with their writing. You should read the stimulus material to your child. Ensure they understand it.

"Hurry up, Katie, you're going to be late!" shouted Katie's mum from downstairs.

Katie was in the middle of getting ready for a very special day. Today was her friend's birthday party.

Everyone in the class was going to be there and she was really looking forward to it.

Katie was going to wear her very best dress and some sparkling new, pink shoes.

When she was finally ready, she tiptoed downstairs where her mum was waiting rather impatiently.

Katie climbed into the car, remembering to check that her dress did not get creased!

Katie felt very excited and throughout the journey she told her mum about the plans.

"There is going to be a magician, party food, hats and games. There's even going to be a bouncy castle," Katie sang merrily.

Katie said goodbye to her mum cheerily and ran into the party.

Long Writing Task

Now you have read *Katie*, you are going to continue the story and write about what happens at the party. Before you write the story, plan what you will write by thinking about:

Who is at the party.

_____

_____

_____

_____

_____

_____

_____

_____

_____

What games Katie and her friends play.

_____

_____

_____

_____

_____

What happens to the magician.

_____

_____

_____

_____

_____

Remember:

1 to write a good beginning

2 to write a clear ending

Read through your plan and think about what you have written. Now write your story.

Short Writing Task

You are going to write a recipe for a birthday cake. Before you write the recipe, plan what it will include by thinking about:

Preparation time: _____

Cooking time: _____

Number of people it will serve: _____

Ingredients: _____

_____

_____

_____

_____

Method: _____

_____

_____

_____

_____

Read through your plan and think about what you have written. Now write the recipe.

Set

B

KEY STAGE 1
Levels 1–3

Spelling Test
Paper

Spelling

Musical Statues

Spelling Test Paper

Musical Statues

Instructions:

- see page 10 for details on how to administer the test

- find a quiet place where you can sit down with your child

- make sure you have all the necessary equipment to complete the test paper

- read the short piece of text on page 63 to your child twice in its entirety

- during the first reading, your child should not write anything on the test paper

- during the second reading, pause after each word to be tested (shown in bold type), to enable your child to write the word in the gap on the test paper

- see page 64 for the spelling test mark conversion chart

Time:

Take as long as necessary to complete the test paper.

	Max.	Number of words correct
Score	20	....

First name ....

Last name ....

Instructions on how to play musical statues.

You will _____ **need** _____: *(practice question)*

    Music

    A stereo

    A _____ to _____

    Lots of _____

    An adult to judge

1 Wait _____ the music to _____.

2 _____ the music _____, dance around the room.

3 As _____ as the music _____, stand as still

   as _____ can.

4 Remember not to _____ at all – be _____

   not to blink your _____ or _____!

5 An adult will _____ around the room _____
   for anyone who is moving.

6 If you are caught moving, then you are _____ and you
   must sit at the side of the room.

7 The winner is the last _____ still _____.

8 _____ luck!

Set

C

KEY STAGE 1
Levels 1–3

Planning Sheets
& Writing Tasks

Writing

The Hare and the Tortoise

Planning Sheets & Writing Tasks

The Hare and the Tortoise

Instructions:

- see pages 6–7 (Long Writing Task) and page 8 (Short Writing Task) for details on how to administer the writing tasks

- find a quiet place where your child can sit down and complete the writing tasks undisturbed

- make sure your child has all the necessary equipment to complete the writing tasks

- make sure your child knows how to plan each task using the planning sheets

- when your child has completed the planning sheet, go through it together

- your child then begins the writing task on a separate sheet of lined paper

- check how your child has done using pages 49–62 of the Answers and Mark Scheme

Time:

Take as long as necessary but aim to complete the Long Writing Task in 45 minutes and the Short Writing Task in 30 minutes.

	Max. Mark	**Actual Mark**
Score	33	

First name ....

Last name ....

The Hare
and the
Tortoise

START

Instructions: This stimulus material is very similar to what your child will be given in school tests. The idea of it is to set the scene of the task and help your child to become inspired with their writing. You should read the stimulus material to your child. Ensure they understand it.

Once upon a time, there lived two very different animals. One of these animals was a grumpy hare and the other was a very clever and gentle tortoise.

One day, in the middle of summer, Hare and Tortoise met each other.

"Why are you always so slow?" Hare asked Tortoise.

"I like my pace," Tortoise replied. "Besides, being fast isn't always everything!"

"Oh yes it is," Hare said.

The two animals argued for a while, then Tortoise suddenly came up with an idea.

"Listen, Hare," he said. "Why don't we have a race? Let's see who will win. How about over the hill and back?"

Hare roared with laughter! "You want to have a race with me? You haven't got a chance!"

"We'll see," Tortoise smiled.

So the next day Tortoise and Hare met for their race. Hare started running immediately. He went away very fast and it wasn't long before he was way out in front.

"Why am I rushing?" Hare thought to himself.

"That silly, slow tortoise won't have even started yet! I know, I'll sit by this tree and have a rest for a while."

So the hare sat down and closed his eyes. He fell into a very deep sleep and eventually began snoring.

Meanwhile, the tortoise was plodding on, and after a very long time he crept past the sleeping hare. Tortoise went on his way, over the hill and back again.

Hare suddenly woke up and tried to race to catch the tortoise up but he'd left it too late. The tortoise had won the race!

The moral of this story is "slow and steady wins the race".

Don't rush things!

Long Writing Task

Now you have read *The Hare and the Tortoise*, you are going to write a similar story, using different animals. Remember in your story that the moral is "slow and steady wins the race". Before you write your story, plan what you will write by thinking about:

Your two animals.

1 _____

2 _____

Where they race.

_____

_____

_____

Who wins.

_____

_____

_____

_____

How they feel at the end of the race.

_____

_____

_____

_____

_____

_____

_____

_____

Read through your plan and think about what you have written. Now write your story.

Short Writing Task

Imagine the hare and the tortoise take part in your school sports day.

Write some rules to tell them both how to take part and behave without arguing.

Your first might be:

1   You must do as you are told the first time.

_____

2   _____

_____

3   _____

_____

4   _____

_____

5   _____

_____

6   _____

_____

Set
C

KEY STAGE 1
Levels 1–3

Spelling Test
Paper

Spelling

Dear Cinderella

Spelling Test Paper

Dear Cinderella

Instructions:

- see page 10 for details on how to administer the test

- find a quiet place where you can sit down with your child

- make sure you have all the necessary equipment to complete the test paper

- read the short piece of text on page 64 to your child twice in its entirety

- during the first reading, your child should not write anything on the test paper

- during the second reading, pause after each word to be tested (shown in bold type), to enable your child to write the word in the gap on the test paper

- see page 64 for the spelling test mark conversion chart

Time:

Take as long as necessary to complete the test paper.

	Max.	**Number of words correct**
Score	20	....

First name ....

Last name ....

_____**Dear**_____ Cinderella, *(practice question)*

We are _____ sorry for being horrible to _____

when you lived with us. We _____ you a lot now that you

_____ in the palace with the prince.

We have to do all the cleaning, _____ and ironing now. It is

_____ not fair! The other day our wicked mother

_____ made us mop the _____.

Last week we had to hang all the washing outside in the _____

and as soon as we had finished our work it began to rain. We felt very

_____, especially as our _____ dresses had

_____ ruined!

We are both hoping that one _____ we will meet a prince just

like you did. When is the prince having _____ ball? We will

make sure we wear the most beautiful glass slippers in the whole world.

We would _____ it if you could _____ and visit us

sometime because we are quite lonely. We would love to hear all about

your new life in the palace. Do you have servants and maids?

Maybe we _____ come and _____ for you one day?

Love _____

The Ugly _____

xxx

Notes

Answers and Mark Scheme

Writing Tasks

Mark Scheme for the Long Tasks

Sentence structure

Assessment focuses: Vary sentences for clarity, purpose and effect.

Band	Description	Mark
A1	Meaningful words and phrases, some of them expressing ideas in sentence-like structures. Some parts of the writing may be abbreviated or disjointed.	*1 mark*
A2	Mainly simple, grammatically accurate statements, often starting with personal subject and past tense action verbs. Writing is often speech-like (e.g. "we did playing"). Repeated pronouns (e.g. "I", "we", "they") or subject nouns (e.g. "the cake …." "the cake"). Use of simple verbs (e.g. "went", "got", "said"). A mixture of simple and compound sentences joined by simple connectives to ensure events are chronologically ordered (e.g. "then we played pass the parcel, then everyone gave me presents, then we had tea"). Some modification of unspecific nouns (e.g. "chocolate cake", "good game", "different presents"). Use of time adverbials (e.g. "first", "then", "after").	*2–3 marks*
A3	Simple connectives (e.g. "and", "but", "then", "so") link clauses into chronological sequence (e.g. "Your letter was lovely, but I'm at school in September, so maybe in August"). Mainly compound sentences, sometimes explaining relationships between ideas (e.g. "Katie had a great birthday because all her friends were there"). Nouns sometimes modified by adjectives (e.g. "slow, lazy tortoise") and verbs modified by adverbs (e.g. "he ran quickly"). Variation in word order and/or position of clauses (e.g. "First our teacher put the music on and we passed the parcel around, then the music stopped").	*4 marks*

Punctuation

Assessment focuses: Write with technical accuracy of syntax and punctuation in phrases, clauses and sentences.

Band	Description	Mark
B1	Some awareness shown of how full stops are used.	*1 mark*
B2	Sentences sometimes demarcated by both capital letters and full stops. Other punctuation may be used (question marks, exclamation marks).	*2–3 marks*
B3	Full stops, capital letters and commas in lists mostly accurate. Question marks and exclamation marks may be used.	*4 marks*

Composition and effect

Assessment focuses: Write imaginative, interesting and thoughtful texts. Produce writing which is appropriate to task, reader and purpose. Organise and present whole texts effectively.

Band	Description	Mark
C1	Some recognisable letters or groups of letters relating to the task. Writing has to be mediated by child, teacher or parent to be understood.	*1–2 marks*
C2	Writing refers to the task and describes actions and events clearly. Events are linked as simple sequences.	*3–4 marks*
C3	Writing relates to the task, with actions detailed in a chronological sequence. There is a simple opening (e.g. "one sunny morning, a mouse was running across the field"). A general concluding statement (e.g. "The mouse was pleased and they ran to the end of the race together"). Some detail included to expand on basic information (e.g. "Next week I'm taking my friends to an athletics tournament. We're playing for a cup"). Some technical vocabulary may be used (e.g. "medal", "finishing tape", "competitors").	*5–7 marks*
C4	Writing exhibits a clear sequence of events, demonstrating a sound opening and ending. The features and stages of the task are clear to the reader. Paragraphing and other organisational features may be evident. Some evidence of viewpoint or personal comment on the task.	*8–10 marks*

Example Writing for the Long Task – "Dear James"

Band A Sentence structure: Band A3, *4 marks*

Band B Punctuation: Band B3, *4 marks*

Band C Composition and effect: Band C4, *9 marks*

Punctuation
Question marks may be used.
Full stops and capital letters accurate.

Composition and effect
Some evidence of viewpoint.

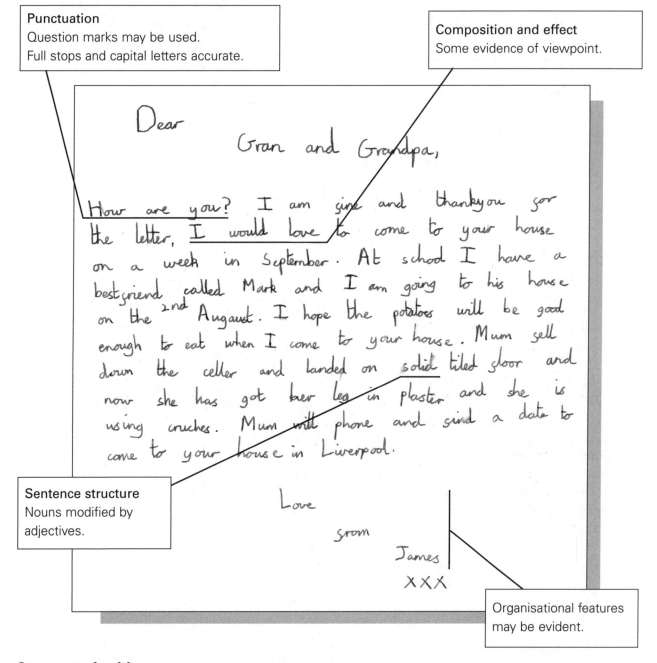

Dear

Gran and Grandpa,

How are you? I am fine and thankyou for the letter, I would love to come to your house on a week in September. At school I have a best friend called Mark and I am going to his house on the 2nd August. I hope the potatoes will be good enough to eat when I come to your house. Mum fell down the celler and landed on solid tiled floor and now she has got her leg in plaster and she is using cruches. Mum will phone and find a date to come to your house in Liverpool.

Love

from

James
XXX

Sentence structure
Nouns modified by adjectives.

Organisational features may be evident.

Summary of writing
- Writing exhibits a clear sequence of events. Sound opening and end.
- Detail included – e.g. "come to your house in Liverpool".

Total marks: 17

Example Writing for the Long Task – "Dear James"

Band A Sentence structure: Band A1, *1 mark*

Band B Punctuation: Band B1, *1 mark*

Band C Composition and effect: Band C1, *1 mark*

Sentence structure
Some parts of the writing may be disjointed.

Composition and effect
Some recognisable letters.
Writing has to be mediated to
be understood.

Punctuation
Some awareness shown of
how full stops are used.

Total marks: 3

Example Writing for the Long Task – "Katie"

Band A Sentence structure: Band A2, *3 marks*

Band B Punctuation: Band B2, *3 marks*

Band C Composition and effect: Band C2, *4 marks*

> **Sentence structure**
> Action verb in the past tense.

The day Katie went to a party

once there lived a little girl her name was called Katie she was nearly exsited at the party. She saw Bob, Betty and Bill Bob was very good very good indead he was exstreanly kind betty was very kind like Bob there was a... magician he jugled with fire! Bill was very nasty ahorrible at the end of the party it was so good she did not want to leave then katie said "ok I'll go home" good girl said her mum and they lived hapely ever after.

> **Punctuation**
> Use of other punctuation.

> **Sentence structure**
> Mixture of simple and compound sentences with clauses joined by 'then'.

Summary of writing
- Writing refers to the chosen activity – e.g. "magician".
- Events are described – e.g. "magician he juggled with fire".

Total marks: 10

Example Writing for the Long Task – "Katie"

Band A Sentence structure: Band A2, *2 marks*

Band B Punctuation: Band B2, *2 marks*

Band C Composition and effect: Band C3, *7 marks*

Composition and effect
Some evidence of viewpoint.
Technical vocabulary may be used.

Sentence structure
Sentence structures often speech-like.

> One bright sunny morning Afternoon geogia arrived at the Party.
> We did playing on the big boney castle, ball caue, swiming Pool, Swing.
> Then we played Pass the Parcel, katie lost I won but I gave the
> Present to Geogia. Then every one gave me Presents I Was Surised
> I opend them I liked The Party. every one liked it. when
> it was time to go i was upset I didnt want
> to leaue so i Creyed. I went to the kitten were
> I got a goody bag. I looked inside I ate my
> cake and Went home.

Punctuation
Sentences sometimes demarcated by both capital letters and full stops.

Sentence structure
Repetition of pronoun I.

Summary of writing
- There is a simple opening and concluding statement.

Total marks: 11

Mark Scheme for the Short Tasks

Sentence structure and punctuation

Assessment focuses: Vary sentences for clarity, purpose and effect. Write with technical accuracy of syntax and punctuation in phrases, clauses and sentences.

Band	Description	Mark
D1	Meaningful words and phrases, some of them expressing ideas in sentence-like structures. Some parts of the writing may be abbreviated or disjointed. Some awareness shown of how full stops are used.	*1 mark*
D2	Mainly simple, grammatically accurate statements or questions. Some clauses joined by and/then (e.g. "Add the eggs and the flour. Mix together, then put in the bowl, then put in the oven"). Some sentences demarcated by capital letters and full stops or question marks.	*2–3 marks*
D3	Consistent use of appropriate format. Nouns modified by adjectives (e.g. "the kind man", "the shining gold medal"). Clauses linked by connectives such as "and", "but", "so". Details are specific (e.g. times of events, place names). Full stops and capital letters mostly accurate, with capital letters used for proper nouns. There may be some use of exclamation marks and question marks. Commas may be used in lists.	*4–5 marks*

Composition and effect

Assessment focuses: Write imaginative, interesting and thoughtful texts. Produce texts which are appropriate to task, reader and purpose. Organise and present whole texts effectively, sequencing and structuring information, ideas and events.

Band	Description	Mark
E1	Some recognisable letters, groups of letters, words or phrases appropriate to the task. The writing needs to be mediated by child, teacher or parent to be understood.	*1 mark*
E2	There is some recognisable information and simple meaning is conveyed through the writing. Vocabulary choices associated with main aspects of the topic (e.g. "race", "winner", "mix", "flour").	*2–3 marks*
E3	Information is generally relevant (e.g. "Remember to turn the oven on before putting in the cake"). Choice of layout is appropriate to the task.	*4–5 marks*
E4	There will be some evidence of viewpoint. Use of headings, line breaks, bullet points or paragraphing. Technical/ambitious vocabulary used. Consistent writing style (e.g. for rules/recipe "You must ...", "Do not ...", "Remember ...", "Always ...").	*6–7 marks*

Example Writing for the Short Task – Postcard

Band D Sentence structure and punctuation: Band D3, *4 marks*

Band E Composition and effect: Band E4, *6 marks*

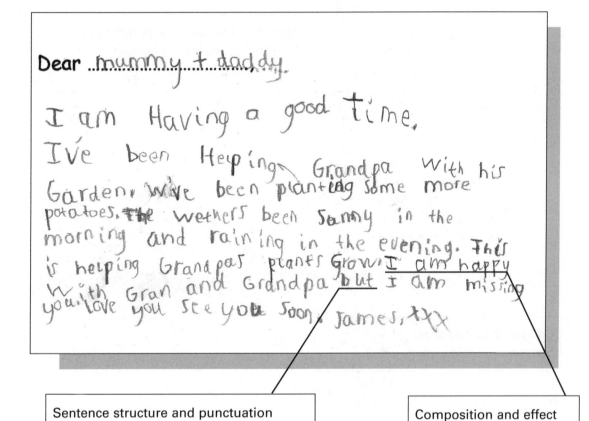

Dear ...mummy..+...daddy.

I am Having a good time. I've been Helping Grandpa with his Garden. we've been planting some more potatoes. The wethers been sunny in the morning and raining in the evening. This is helping Grandpas plants Grow. I am happy with Gran and Grandpa but I am missing you. love you see you soon. James, xxx

Sentence structure and punctuation
Clauses linked by connectives.

Composition and effect
Evidence of viewpoint.

Summary of writing
• Consistent use of appropriate format.

Total marks: 10

Example Writing for the Short Task –

Recipe for Making a Cake

Band D Sentence structure and punctuation: Band D1, *1 mark*

Band E Composition and effect: Band E1, *1 mark*

Sentence structure and punctuation
Meaningful words and phrases.

Composition and effect
Some recognisable letters, words.

Summary of writing
• Writing has to be mediated to be understood.

Total marks: 2

Example Writing for the Short Task – Writing Rules

Band D Sentence structure and punctuation: Band D2, *2 marks*

Band E Composition and effect: Band E4, *6 marks*

Composition and effect
Use of ambitious vocabulary.

Sentence structure and punctuation
Use of "and" to join clauses.

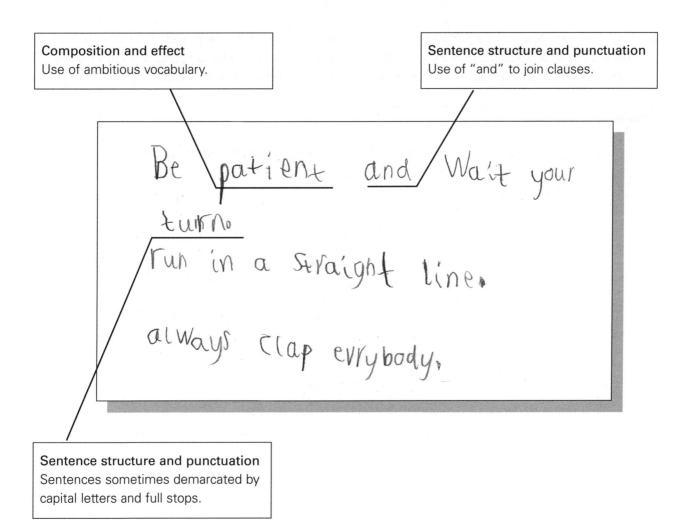

Be patient and Wait your
turn.
run in a straight line.

always clap evrybody,

Sentence structure and punctuation
Sentences sometimes demarcated by capital letters and full stops.

Summary of writing
- Consistent writing style.
- Use of line breaks.
- Accurate statements used.

Total marks: 8

Handwriting

There is no separate test to assess your child's handwriting. This makes it much easier! A score out of 3 will be given, by assessing the handwriting from the writing tasks.

1   Look at the long and short writing tasks. Choose a few lines where your child has done their best handwriting. This will be the handwriting to assess.

2   Use the table below to match your child's handwriting to a band.

3   Use the examples of children's handwriting on pages 61 and 62. These provide examples of how the writing in different bands may look. Do not worry if your child's handwriting does not exactly match any example. These are only a guide. Use your judgement to find the best fit.

Band	Description	Mark
F1	Writing is legible, letters are usually correctly formed and orientated. Upper and lower case letters are not generally mixed within the word.	*1 mark*
F2	Letters are correctly formed and orientated. Writing shows some evidence of being controlled – letters are generally neat and regular in size. Ascenders and descenders are regular in size.	*2 marks*
F3	Letters are correctly formed and orientated. Handwriting is neat and regular in size. There is evidence of fluency and the ability to join letters.	*3 marks*

Example Handwriting

Example Handwriting – *0 marks*

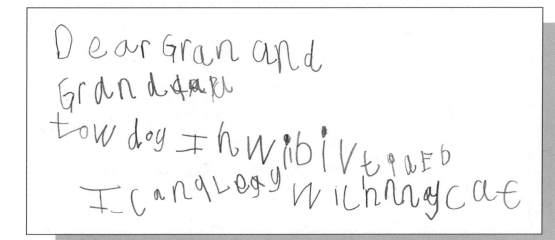

Example Handwriting – *1 mark*

Example Handwriting – *2 marks*

and there was a bouncy castle and a
swimming pool I went in all oss them and
the magizene did a slip up and disapend

Example Handwriting – *3 marks*

Dear Gran and Grandpa,
I'm fine thankyou, how are you?
Are you going to grow anything else in your vegtable
patch, such as tomatoes, pears, fruit or anything else.
I'm glad the weather is nice there, but it's so cold
here. We have to have the heating, and fire on to make
the house warm. She is great, my new teacher, her name's

Spelling Test Passages

Pete's Big Feet

Say "Hi!" to Pete. He is **ever** so sweet.

He is **never** mean and **always** smiles at **people** he meets.

He remembers to say **please** and thank you, too. At **weekends**, Pete likes to help **friends down** his street. He tidies up garden weeds and sweeps floors for them.

When it is sunny, Pete **likes** to fish at Wheat Field Stream.

But his favourite meal is not fish. It is lean meat **with** peas. And if he has a treat, it has to be cheese.

You see, Pete likes the same **things** as **many boys**.

He loves **games** with mates and **seeing** movies. He tries to be neat and tidy in his best **green** jeans.

Above his knees, Pete **looks** like **anyone** you **might** meet. But **below** the knees, he makes some squeal.

"Are those real feet?" some say.

Others ask "Can I have a feel? Wow, **your** feet are unreal!"

You see, Pete has big, no, huge, no, giant-sized feet!

Musical Statues

Instructions on how to play musical statues.

You will need:

Music

A stereo

A **place** to **dance**

Lots of **children**

An adult to judge

1 Wait **for** the music to **begin**.

2 **When** the music **starts**, dance around the room.

3 As **soon** as the music **stops**, stand as still as **you** can.

4 Remember not to **move** at all – be **careful** not to blink your **eyes** or **smile**!

5 An adult will **walk** around the room **looking** for anyone who is moving.

6 If you are caught moving, then you are **out** and you must sit at the side of the room.

7 The winner is the last **person** still **dancing**.

8 **Good** luck!

Dear Cinderella

Dear Cinderella,

We are **so** sorry for being horrible to **you** when you lived with us. We **miss** you a lot now that you **live** in the palace with the prince.

We have to do all the cleaning, **washing** and ironing now. It is **just** not fair! The other day our wicked mother **even** made us mop the **floor**.

Last week we had to hang all the washing outside in the **garden** and as soon as we had finished our work it began to rain. We felt very **cross**, especially as our **new** dresses had **been** ruined!

We are both hoping that one **day** we will meet a prince just like you did. When is the prince having **another** ball? We will make sure we wear the most beautiful glass slippers in the whole world.

We would **like** it if you could **come** and visit us sometime because we are quite lonely. We would love to hear all about your new life in the palace. Do you have servants and maids?

Maybe we **should** come and **work** for you one day?

Love **from**

The Ugly **Sisters**

XXX

Using the Spelling Test Score

Your child will have a score out of 20. Use the table below to convert this score into a mark out of 7.

Number of correct words	0–3	4–7	8–11	12–14	15–16	17–18	19–20
Marks	1	2	3	4	5	6	7